Look at Me I'm Learning Spanish

(A STORY FOR AGES 3-6)

By Daniel Williamson

Illustrated by Kleverton Monteiro

DW

First published in 2019 by Daniel Williamson
www.danielwilliamson.co.uk
This edition published in 2020

ISBN 978-1-9162563-0-9

DW

www.danielwilliamson.co.uk

This book is dedicated
to my daughter
Carmela

I'm a small person in a big, big world!

¡Soy una persona pequeña en un mundo muy, muy grande!

I know people bigger than me.
Bigger people know more things because
they start to learn when they are small.

Conozco personas mayores que yo.
Los mayores saben más cosas porque empiezan
a aprender cuando son pequeños.

Not everyone speaks English like me. Some bigger people speak Spanish, some speak two languages!

No todo el mundo habla inglés como yo. ¡Algunas personas mayores hablan español, otras hablan dos idiomas!

I want to learn Spanish too so I can speak to Spanish speaking people and make even more friends!

¡Yo también quiero aprender español para poder hablar con personas que lo hablan y así hacer muchos más amigos!

First I'm going to learn to count using the peas on my plate.

Primero, voy a aprender a contar usando los guisantes de mi plato.

Now I know how to count to ten! Look at me
I'm learning Spanish, learning Spanish is Fun!

Ahora ya sé contar hasta diez. ¡Mírame, estoy
aprendiendo español! ¡Aprender español es divertido!

I wonder what to say if I meet a Spanish speaking person? I think I would say - “Hello, how are you?” Then they would say - “I’m fine thanks and you?”

Me pregunto que diría si me encuentro con alguien que habla español.
Creo que diría: –Hola, ¿cómo estás?
Y me contestaría: –Bien, gracias ¿y tú?

Then I would need to tell them my name. I would say - "Hello, my name is ______________, what's your name?"

Después tendría que decirle cómo me llamo. Diría —me llamo ______________, ¿y tú?

Now I want to tell them my age and ask how old they are. Let's see if I can remember the numbers!

Ahora quiero decirle cuántos años tengo y preguntarle cuántos años tiene. ¡A ver si puedo acordarme de los números!

ONE
UNO

TWO
DOS

THREE
TRES

FOUR
CUATRO

FIVE
CINCO

SIX
SEIS

SEVEN
SIETE

EIGHT
OCHO

NINE
NUEVE

TEN
DIEZ

I am _______ years old, how old are you?

Tengo_________años, ¿y tú cuántos tienes?

Look at me I'm learning Spanish!
Learning Spanish is fun!

¡Mírame, estoy aprendiendo español!
¡Aprender español es divertido!

I need to know how to say the things I like and the things I don't like, let's try some sentences!

Tengo que saber decir las cosas que me gustan y las que no me gustan, ¡Vamos a probar con algunas frases!

I like sunny days. I like to go to the park and play on the slide and swings!

¡Me gustan los días soleados, ir al parque, jugar en el tobogán y columpiarme!

I also love playing with my friends outside. Sometimes we play football, sometimes we play hide and seek!

¡También me gusta jugar con mis amigos en la calle. Algunas veces jugamos al fútbol; otras, al escondite!

I don't like when it's rainy and windy so I go to the cinema, watch cartoons and eat popcorn.

No me gusta cuando llueve y hace viento, así que voy al cine, veo dibujos animados o como palomitas.

My favourite thing to do is go for a picnic.
I like eating apple slices but I prefer bananas!

Lo que más me gusta hacer es ir de picnic.
¡Me gustan las manzanas,
pero prefiero los plátanos!

Last time I went to the park I saw a huge rainbow.
Let's see if I can remember all the colours!

La última vez que fui al parque vi un gran arcoiris.
¡Vamos a ver si puedo recordar todos los colores!

RED ROJO

ORANGE NARANJA

YELLOW AMARILLO

GREEN VERDE

BLUE AZUL

INDIGO AÑIL

VIOLET MORADO

The colours of the rainbow are red, orange, yellow, green, blue, indigo and violet!

¡Los colores del arcoiris son: rojo, naranja, amarillo, verde, azul, añil y morado.

Look at me I'm learning Spanish!
Learning Spanish is fun!

¡Mírame, estoy aprendiendo español!
¡Aprender español es divertido!

At home I have some different pets and they are different colours too! I have a brown dog, a black and white cat and a grey rabbit.

En casa tengo diferentes mascotas, ¡y cada una es de un color diferente! Tengo un perro marrón; un gato blanco y negro, y un conejo gris.

My dog likes me to throw his ball for him, he always brings it back, it's his favourite game!

A mi perro le gusta que le lance la pelota, siempre me la devuelve, ¡es su juego favorito!

My cat likes to sleep on the sofa all
day, he's a very lazy cat!

A mi gato le gusta dormir en el sillón
todo el día, ¡es muy perezoso!

My rabbit lives in the garden, he eats carrots all day, they help him see better at night time!

Mi conejo vive en el jardín, come zanahorias todo el día, ¡lo ayudan a ver mejor por la noche!

At night time I get into my pyjamas, I love getting into bed
for a story, then I close my eyes and slowly fall asleep,
ready to learn more Spanish tomorrow...

Por la noche me pongo el pijama. Me encanta meterme
en la cama y que me lean un cuento, después cierro
los ojos y me voy quedando dormido, preparado para
aprender más español mañana...

THE
END
FIN

This author has developed a bilingual book series designed to introduce children to a number of new languages from a very young age.

If you enjoyed reading this story, you will undoubtedly like popular rhyming picture books from this author which are also currently available.

Message from the Author

I'd like to say a massive thank you to every single child and adult that read one of my books! My dream is to bring cultures together through fun illustrations, imagination and creativity via the power of books.

If you would like to join me on this journey, please visit my website danielwilliamson.co.uk where each email subscriber receives a free ebook to keep or we will happily send to a friend of your choice as a gift!

Nothing makes me happier than a review on the platform you purchased my book telling me where my readers are from! Also, please click on my links below and follow me to join my ever-growing online family! Remember there is no time like the present and the present is a gift!

Yours gratefully

Daniel Williamson

@danwauthor

@DanWAuthor

Made in the USA
Middletown, DE
09 April 2023